▲ Name _____

Match it!

You will need: one picture board and a set of matching cards (below) for each player, scissors.

Match the cards to the pictures on the board.

Animal or not?

You will need: crayons.

Look at this picture. Colour the things that are alive.

Animals
Teachers' notes

Aims of this book

This book provides photocopiable activities for children aged three to five to support the development of science concepts and skills. No special resources are needed, other than those usually to be found in nurseries or reception classes. The activities prepare for later learning in the National Curriculum/Scottish 5–14 Guidelines.

Developing science skills

Children should be involved as much as possible in practical, hands-on activities. Sorting and classifying, looking for similarities and differences, will help develop observational skills. The children's main method of recording will probably be verbal, but these sheets may be used as a simple way of recording or reinforcing the practical experiences.

Safety precautions

Encourage children to develop a caring attitude when dealing with living things. Check for allergies before handling animals and always wash hands thoroughly afterwards. For further information see *Be Safe!*, published by the Association for Science Education, College Lane, Hatfield, Hertfordshire AL10 9AA.
NB Young children may need support in activities where cutting skills are required.

Notes on individual activities

Page 3: Match it

This simple matching game will encourage children to appreciate the variety of animal life. Cut out the second set of pictures and match to the picture board, or match model animals to the pictures. Mount the pictures on card and cover with sticky-backed plastic to make a lotto game.

Page 4: Animal or not?

Children need to be able to distinguish between living and non-living things. To extend this, cut out pictures of living things and non-living things from old magazines and sort them into sets.

Page 5: Furry friends

Children should begin to appreciate that different creatures have different types of coat or skin. If possible, handle real animals beforehand to develop appropriate vocabulary such as rough, smooth, hairy, furry, warm, shell, scales.

Page 6: My caterpillar

Prepare by looking at caterpillars under a magnifying glass. Making a caterpillar out of bottle tops or circles will help children understand that the body is made up of segments.

Page 7: Fishy scales

Look closely at fish, noticing the pattern that the scales make. You can enlarge the sheet for a group of children to work on together.

Page 8: Matchstick hedgehog

Discuss how hedgehogs are different from other creatures and why they have spines. Make model hedgehogs using matchsticks stuck into a potato for spines, with a shiny button for an eye.

Page 9: Snails

You can keep snails inside quite easily for a short time (a week) in an aquarium with damp peat, stones and some suitable plant life. Are all shells the same? Roll the dough into a sausage, then place a spiral and body shape over the snail on the page. You could cut out the spiral to hang up.

Page 10: How many legs?

To prepare, look at animals in real life if possible. Encourage the children to observe closely, so they begin to appreciate that different creatures may have different numbers of legs.

Page 11: Where's my tail?

This activity encourages children to observe more closely and to realise that different animals have different types of tail.

Page 12: Bird wings

This sheet will help children develop an appreciation of the rich variety of life. Discuss why the birds have different kinds of feathers for flight and for warmth.

Page 13: Whose ears?

Ears are important for alerting animals to danger or potential food. Prepare templates of the ears at the bottom by mounting on card and cutting out. The children can draw around these to complete the animal heads. Some children may be able to cut and stick the ears.

Page 14: Tracks

On a muddy or snowy day, go outside and find tracks. The pictures can be a straightforward matching task, or be made into a game of Snap using two or three sets of cards. Identical cards, or the animals and their tracks, can be matched.

Page 15: Snail trails
Animals' tracks or trails show us where they have been. Collect some snails and let them crawl over black paper. Outline the trails with chalk.

Page 16: Heads and tails
There are similarities and differences between animals – for example, many have tails but the tails may be different. The children will have fun making their own animals by mixing the parts.

Page 17: Jigsaw
This sheet will help children to recognise the 'structure' of some animals. Compare this structure with that of other creatures, such as a worm. Make a jigsaw by cutting up the picture.

Page 18: Animal puppets
Identify each of the animals and talk about the sort of noise each makes. Colour the puppets, cut them out and stick the ends of each strip together to fit round a finger. For younger children, make the strip long enough to go round four fingers. Sing 'Old MacDonald'.

Page 19: Who lives on the farm?
Talk about where different animals can be found. Ideally, the activity should follow a visit to a farm or a play session with the model farm.

Page 20: What do you see in the air?
Go outside to see what is flying or floating in the air. Are animals in the air all the time or do they come down to earth sometimes? Why is this?

Page 21: Who lives in the sea?
For children who aren't familiar with the sea, discussion based on good pictures or videos should take place before this activity.

Page 22: In the garden
Go outside and look for creatures seen in gardens. Collect and handle creatures carefully, returning them to their habitat as soon as possible. Make tissue-paper flowers to stick on the sheets and hide little creatures under the leaves.

Page 23: Where does my pet live?
Photocopy the sheet several times and mount on card to make an animal lotto game; or children can cut out their own set of the animal cards to match with the right homes. Talk about pet care.

Page 24: Underground
This activity will help children to realise that some animals live underground. Some children may

know other creatures that have similar homes. Introduce new words, such as warren.

Page 25: Where might you find them?
Help children to think about the environments in which animals live and how they are adapted to that habitat. Colour the animal pictures and then cut them out and stick them in the appropriate place on the main picture.

Page 26: Find the caterpillars
Many small creatures are coloured to match or blend into their surroundings for protection. Others are brightly coloured in order to warn predators that they are poisonous. Colour some caterpillars to stand out and others to blend in.

Page 27: Hide it
Consider how some animals are coloured for protection. Copy the sheet, cut out the butterfly and mount on to card to form a template. Next, give each child a sheet and a template and ask them to choose some patterned paper. Using the template, cut out a butterfly from the paper and cut out another square of patterned paper to stick on to their sheet. Place the patterned butterfly over the square to 'hide' it. For a 3-D effect, mount the butterfly on a card roll or box.

Page 28: Whose baby?
Talk about the names that some of these baby animals have. Draw lines to match each baby to its mother or cut out the pictures and match the pairs. Use the pictures to make a Snap game.

Page 29: Tadpole to frog
This activity helps to reinforce the cyclical nature of growth and reproduction. Mount the two circles on to card and fix together with a paper-fastener, so that the top circle may be rotated on the bottom one to show the stages of growth. Decorate the top circle to represent where a frog might live. Turn the circle clockwise.

Page 30: Who laid the egg?
Some types of animals lay eggs, but others don't. Discuss human babies and how they differ from those of other animals. Use washed and crushed eggshells to collage the shell in the picture, and use yellow cotton wool for a fluffy chick.

Page 31: Baby's hungry
Many baby animals depend on their parents for food and shelter. The parent bird's beak is left empty, so that the children can decide what food might be being offered to the chicks.

Page 32: Bird diary
A bird table is a good focus for observation work. Carry out this activity for ten minutes each day.

Furry friends

You will need: scraps of fabric including fur fabric, glue.

Choose the right material to cover the kitten.

My caterpillar

You will need: buttons, milk-bottle tops, paper circles, glue.

Choose the materials to make your caterpillar.

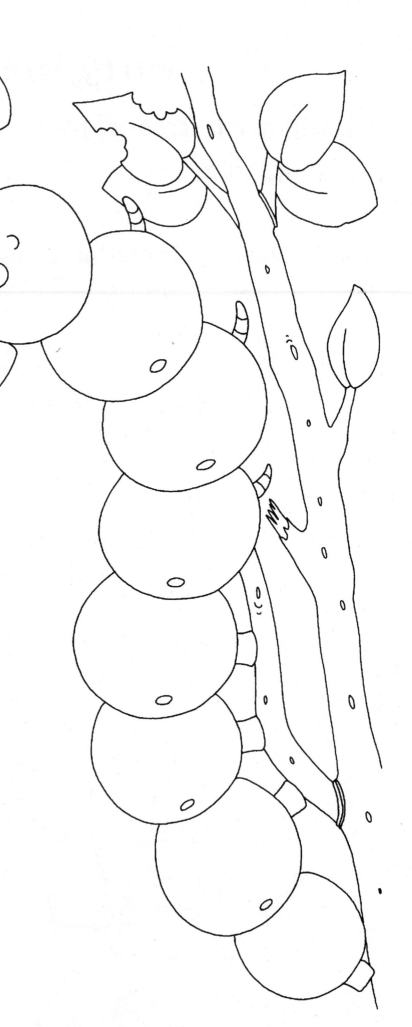

Fishy scales

You will need: Small tissue circles, small sticky paper circles or large sequins, glue.

Stick circles on to the fish to give it scales.

Matchstick hedgehog

You will need: matchsticks, glue,
a dark-coloured button.

Stick the matchsticks on to the picture to
make a hedgehog. Use a button for its eye.

Snails

You will need: play dough.

Make the shape of the snail's shell with play dough.

How many legs?

You will need: scissors, pipe cleaners, glue.

Give each animal the right number of legs.

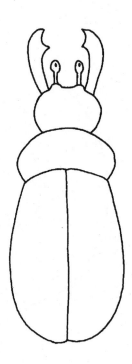

Where's my tail?

You will need: string, cotton wool, scissors, glue.

Give each animal the right kind of tail.

Bird wings

You will need: an assortment of clean feathers, glue.

Make some wings for your bird.

Whose ears?

You will need: crayons, scissors, glue.

Match each animal with
the right pair of ears.

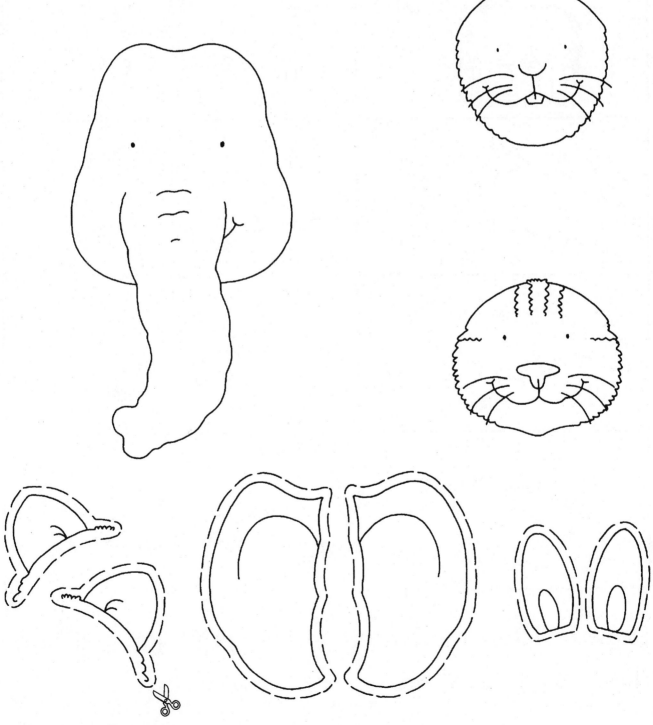

Tracks

You will need: crayons, scissors.

Can you match the animal to the track it has made?

Draw a picture of yourself and the print you make on the back of this sheet.

Snail trails

You will need: a pencil.

Which snail gets the lettuce?
Follow the trail with your pencil to find out.

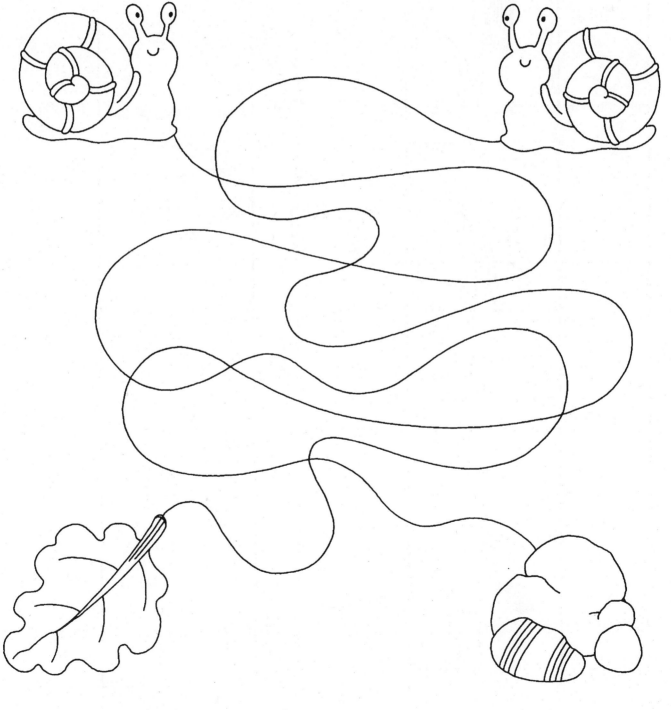

Heads and tails

You will need: crayons, scissors.

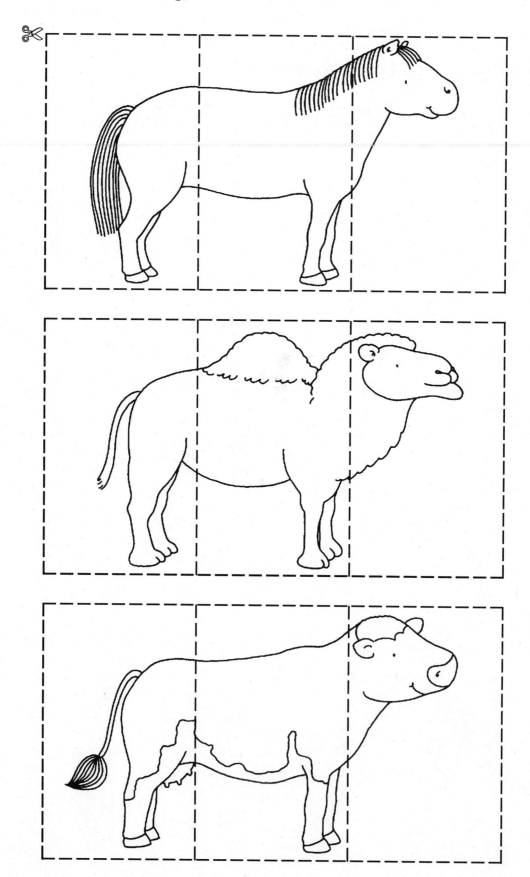

Jigsaw

You will need: scissors, crayons.

Make an animal jigsaw.

Animal puppets

You will need: crayons, scissors, glue.

Colour each animal and cut out the strips.
Stick the ends of each strip together with glue
to make a finger or hand puppet.

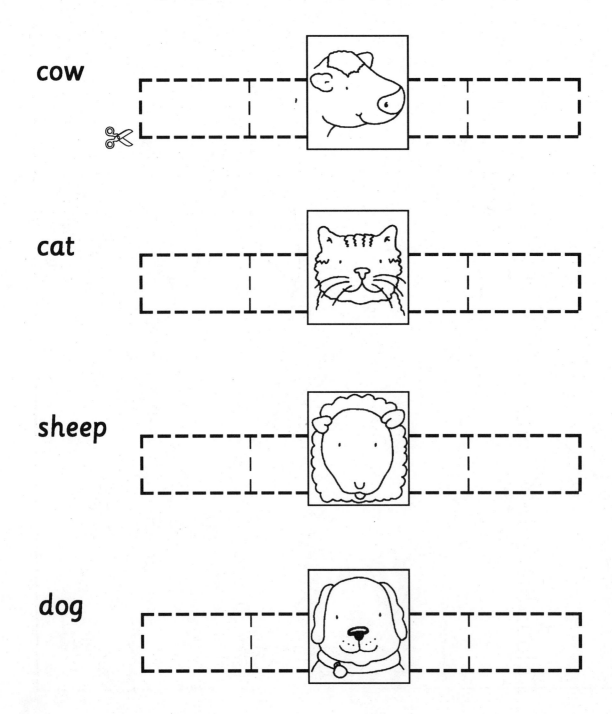

cow

cat

sheep

dog

Who lives on the farm?

You will need: crayons.

Colour the animals that live on a farm.

What do you see in the air?

You will need: crayons.

Colour the things you see in the air.

Which is the odd one out?

Who lives in the sea?

You will need: crayons.

Colour the creatures that live in the sea.

Which is the odd one out?

In the garden

You will need: crayons.

Colour the creatures you would find in the garden.

Which animals shouldn't be there?

Where does my pet live?

You will need: a homes picture board and set of animal cards for each player, scissors.

Match the pets to their homes.

Underground

You will need: a pencil.

Help the mother rabbit to find her babies.
Use your pencil to find the way.

Where might you find them?

You will need: crayons, scissors, glue.

Stick the animal cards into the right places
on the picture.

Find the caterpillars

You will need: crayons.

Can you find the caterpillars? Colour them.

How many caterpillars did you find?

Hide it

You will need: heavily patterned wrapping paper or wallpaper, scissors, pencils, glue, card.

Hide the butterfly on the patterned paper.

Whose baby?

You will need: a pencil, scissors.

Match each baby to its mother.

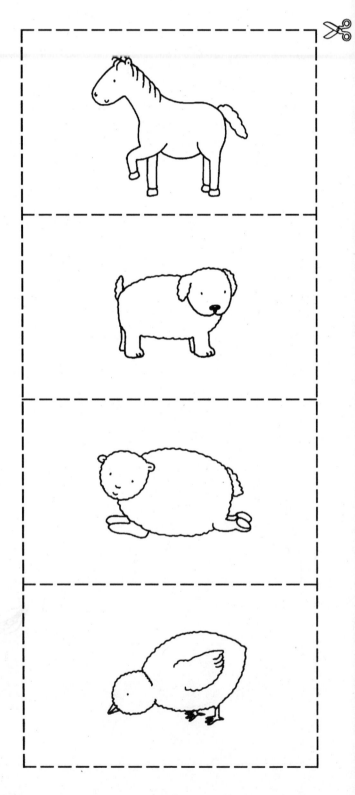

Tadpole to frog

You will need: scissors, crayons, a paper-fastener, card, glue.

Cut these out to make a picture wheel.

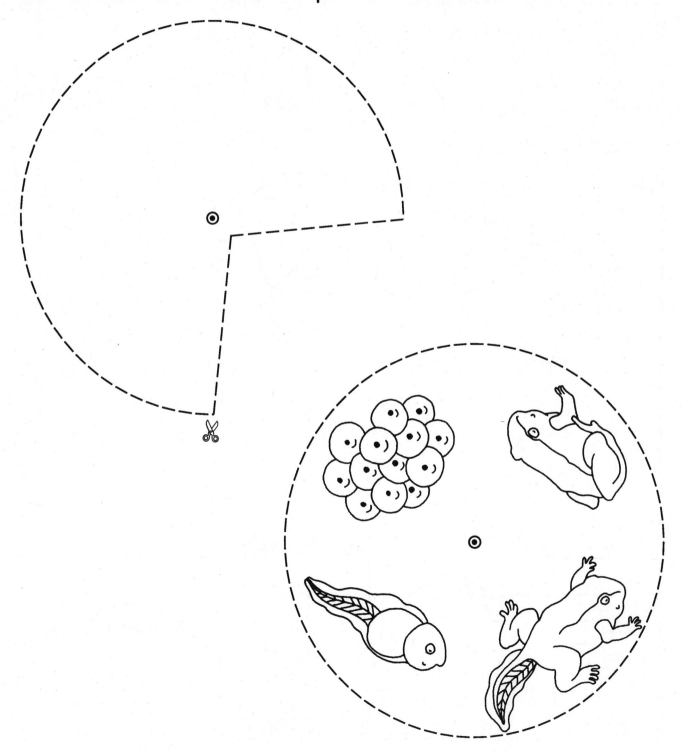

Who laid the egg?

You will need: crayons, washed crushed eggshells, glue, yellow cotton wool, black and red shiny paper.

Use the materials to decorate the picture.

Colour the animal that laid the egg.

Baby's hungry

You will need: straw/raffia, feathers, wool, glue, fabric.

Decorate the picture with your materials.

Bird diary

You will need: crayons, a pencil, an outdoor bird feeder.

Did any birds visit
the feeder today?
✓ Yes   ✗ No

If **yes**,
write how many you saw.

Day	✓ ✗	Number
Monday		
Tuesday		
Wednesday		
Thursday		
Friday		